Sandy Creek
NEW YORK

An Imprint of Sterling Publishing
387 Park Avenue South
New York, NY 10016

SANDY CREEK and the distinctive Sandy Creek logo are registered
trademarks of Barnes & Noble, Inc.

Text © 2012 by QEB Publishing, Inc.
Illustrations © 2012 by QEB Publishing, Inc.

This 2013 edition published by Sandy Creek.

Consultant: Fiona Moss RE Adviser, RE Today Services
Editor: Cathy Jones
Designer: Chris Fraser

ISBN 978-1-4351-5228-1

Manufactured in Guangdong, China
Lot #:
10 9 8 7 6 5 4 3 2 1
08/13

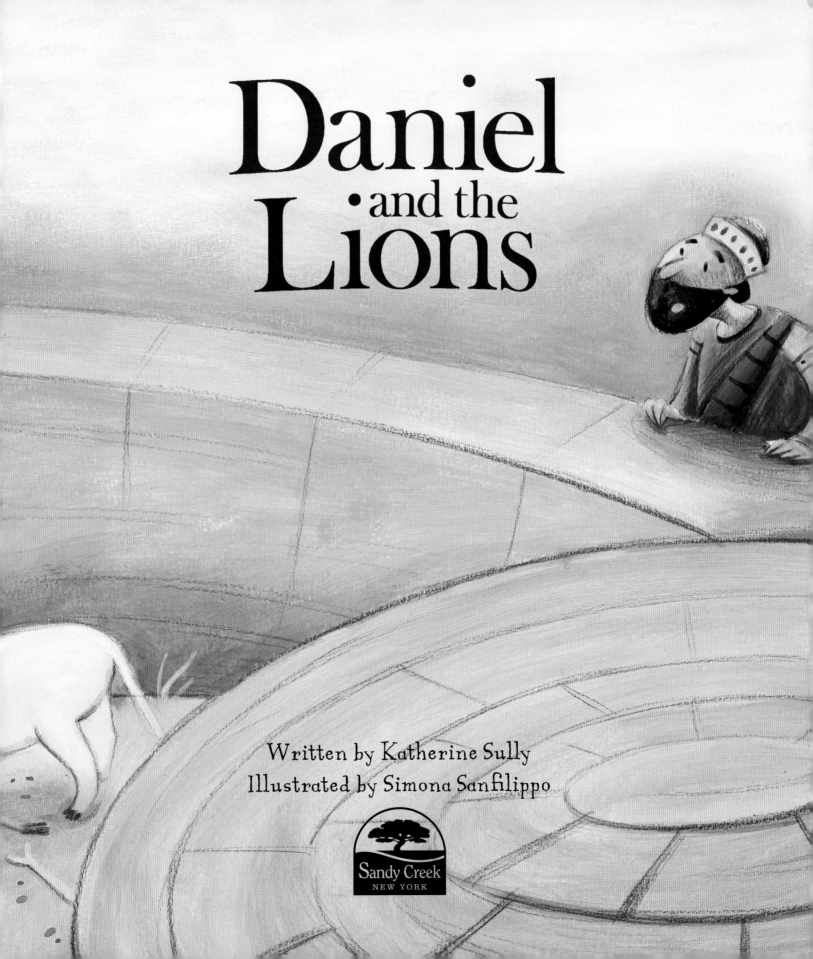

Daniel
and the
Lions

Written by Katherine Sully
Illustrated by Simona Sanfilippo

Sandy Creek
NEW YORK

Daniel was an important man. He was one of three ministers chosen by the king to help him rule the land.

Daniel worked hard. He soon became the king's favorite.

One day, the king decided to put Daniel in charge of everyone.

The other two ministers were angry.

"Why should Daniel be more important than us?" they grumbled.

"He's not even from this land," whispered one.

"And he only praises his own god!" whispered the other.

Will Daniel survive a night with the lions?
Read the story of Daniel who disobeyed the king
and ended up in the lions' den!

The perfect introduction to Old Testament stories
for young children, **My First Bible Stories** combine
simple retellings with fabulous illustrations.

Sandy Creek
NEW YORK

Noah's Ark

Joseph's Colorful Coat

Moses in the Bulrushes

David and Goliath

Jonah and the Big Fish

U.S. $7.99
ISBN 978-1-4351-5228-1

50799

9 781435 152281

Manufactured in China

Together, they came up with
a plan to get rid of Daniel.

The two ministers went to see the king.
"Oh, King, you are so great!" they cried.
"Make a law saying that everyone
should praise only you for thirty days!"

The king liked to be praised,
so he listened to them.

"Whoever breaks the law must then
be thrown into the lions' den," they said.
The king agreed to make it the law.

For thirty days, everyone
praised the king.

But Daniel went home,
knelt at the window,
and praised God,
just as he always did.

The king made a new law.

From that time on, everyone in the land would worship God. "God's law is the law," he said.

Grrr!

Next Steps

Now that you've read the story...what do you remember?

* Who was Daniel?
* Why was he the king's favorite?
* Why did Daniel pray to God?
* Where did Daniel end up?
* What happened when Daniel was in the lions' den?
* How did Daniel get out of the den?

What does the story tell us?
We don't have to be afraid of scary things, because God is looking after us.

The two ministers were spying on Daniel.

When they saw him praising God, they went straight to the king.

"Oh, King, you are so great!" they cried.
"Daniel praised his god. He has broken the law."
When the king heard this he was very sad.

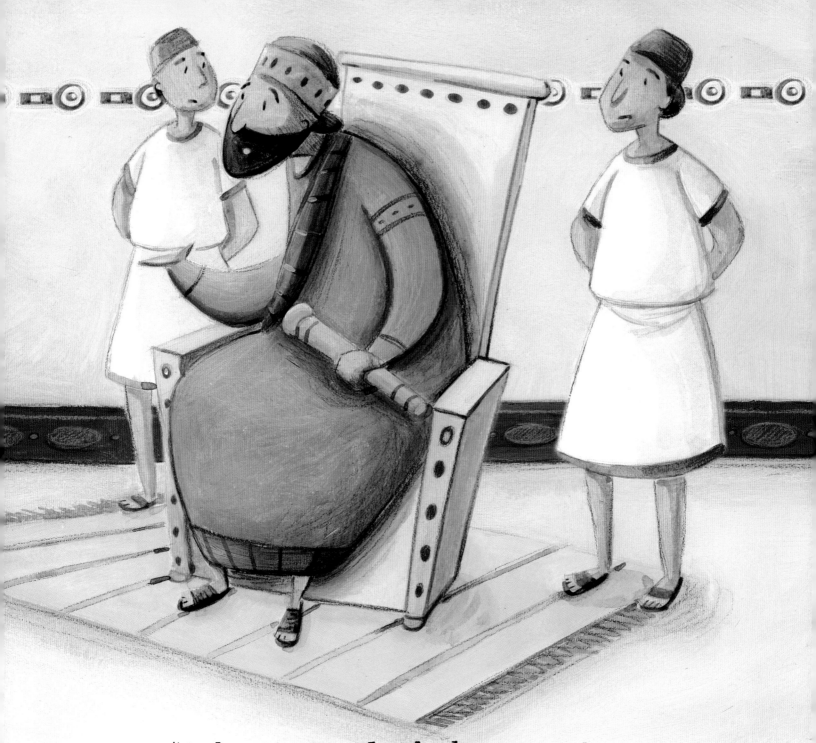

"Whoever breaks the law must then
be thrown into the lions' den," they said.
"The law is the law," sighed the king.

Daniel was taken to the deep, dark den.
Inside, the lions prowled and growled.

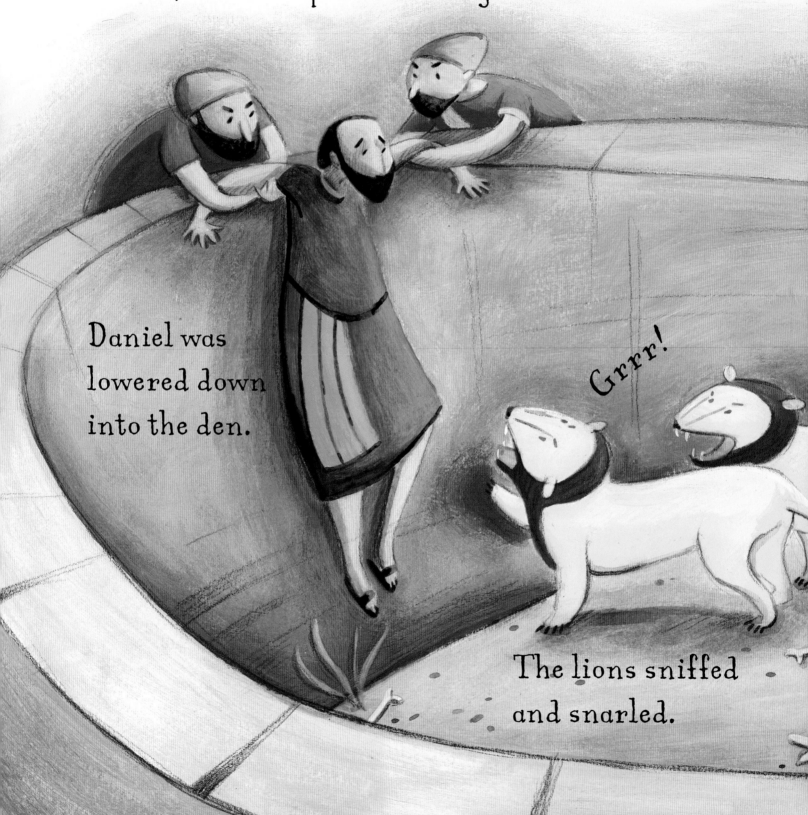

Daniel was lowered down into the den.

Grrr!

The lions sniffed and snarled.

The king looked down into the den. "I hope your God takes care of you, Daniel," he called sadly.

A big rock was rolled over the den
so that there was no escape.

Daniel sat in the gloomy den.
The lions circled around him.

Then an angel appeared,
and the lions settled down.

The king went back to his palace.

He couldn't eat.

He couldn't work.

He couldn't sleep.

All night long he tossed and turned in his bed.

The next morning, as soon as the sun came up, the king hurried to the lions' den. He gave orders to roll back the stone.

"Daniel!" he called, "has God saved you from the lions?"

"Oh, King, you are great!" called Daniel. "God sent an angel to tame the lions. I am safe."

The king was so happy as Daniel was lifted from the den. There wasn't a mark on him!